Monsters From the

Introduction

Shadows and dark corners aren't scary.
It's the crazy, gnashing monsters
that live there that are scary.

This book covers four of these grim nasties
from different shadowy places.

The Underbed Bug isn't as nasty as it looks.
The Creaky Toastmuncher creeps about in the night.
The Just-Behind-You Horse is always just out of sight.
The End has seen more films than most monsters.

Published by CGP

Contents

The Underbed Bug

The Underbed Bug lurks in the dark, shadowy mess underneath beds.

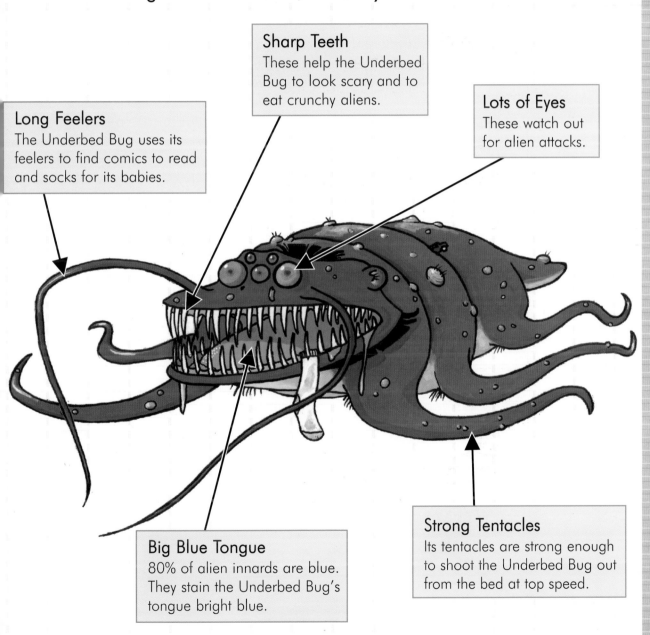

Sharp Teeth
These help the Underbed Bug to look scary and to eat crunchy aliens.

Lots of Eyes
These watch out for alien attacks.

Long Feelers
The Underbed Bug uses its feelers to find comics to read and socks for its babies.

Big Blue Tongue
80% of alien innards are blue. They stain the Underbed Bug's tongue bright blue.

Strong Tentacles
Its tentacles are strong enough to shoot the Underbed Bug out from the bed at top speed.

The Underbed Bug

Food

It's cold in space. That's why aliens come to Earth to steal our blankets.

Aliens get very chilly, zipping about in their flying saucers.

They beam down to Earth to steal our blankets and slippers...

...but if an alien picks a room with an Underbed Bug, they'll be eaten.

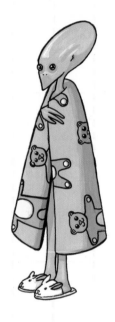

Enemies

If a vacuum cleaner gets too close, the Underbed Bug can get sucked up.

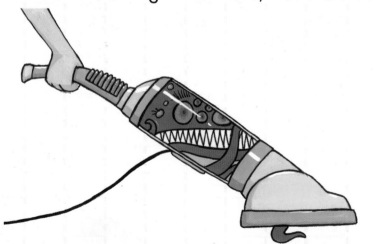

Protect your Underbed Bug...

...don't vacuum near the edge of the bed.

The Underbed Bug

Catching Food

The Underbed Bug waits and watches, then leaps and munches. All very quietly.

1. For most of the time the Underbed Bug just waits, quietly reading comics.

2. They like humans because humans invented socks. They never eat humans.

3. When an alien arrives the Underbed Bug puts down its comic. Then it attacks.

4. It all happens without a sound. All you might find in the morning is a few leftover crumbs of alien.

 # The Underbed Bug

Life Cycle

Baby Underbed Bugs go out into the world hidden in a sock.

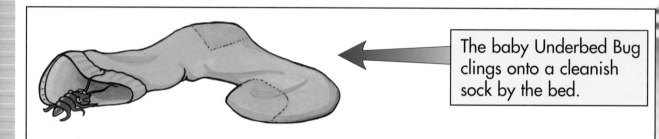

The baby Underbed Bug clings onto a cleanish sock by the bed.

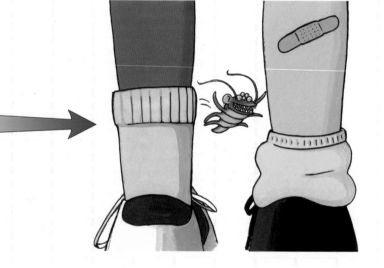

When the baby sees a different cleanish sock it leaps over and grabs on.

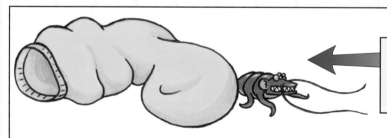

The new sock is kicked off and the young Underbed Bug scuttles under the bed — its new home.

The Underbed Bug

How to Spot One

Underbed Bugs are great at hiding, even in a small heap of mess.

Photo before the Underbed Bug moved in.

Don't poke around too much — they like humans, but they do have very pointy teeth.

Photo after the Underbed Bug moved in.

Look out for red eyes, green tentacles and white, pointy teeth.

This picture was taken with a heat camera. Hot things show up red.

These are the things to look out for.

The Creaky Toastmuncher

Creaky Toastmunchers are very shy. That doesn't stop them looking scary.

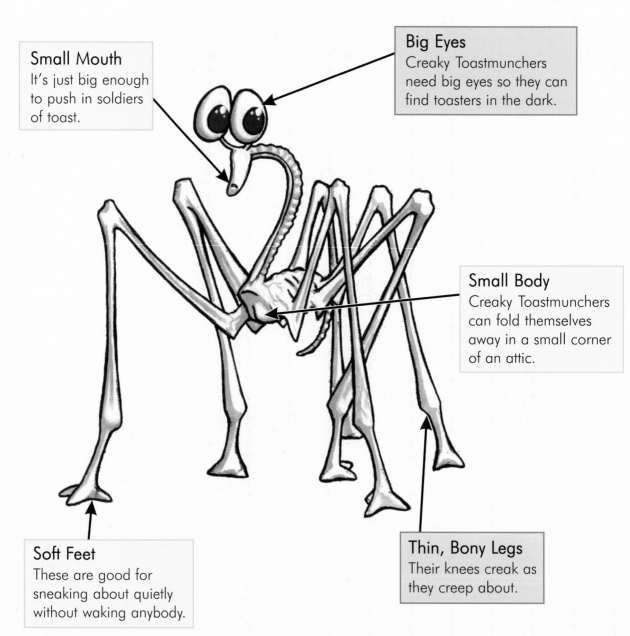

Small Mouth
It's just big enough to push in soldiers of toast.

Big Eyes
Creaky Toastmunchers need big eyes so they can find toasters in the dark.

Small Body
Creaky Toastmunchers can fold themselves away in a small corner of an attic.

Soft Feet
These are good for sneaking about quietly without waking anybody.

Thin, Bony Legs
Their knees creak as they creep about.

6

The Creaky Toastmuncher

Food

The name Creaky **Toastmuncher** gives it away really... It munches toast.

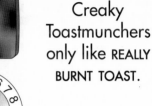

Creaky Toastmunchers only like REALLY BURNT TOAST.

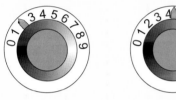  

Enemies

Creaky Toastmunchers can be eaten by Underbed Bugs.

If a Creaky Toastmuncher strays too near to a bed, the Underbed Bug will pounce.

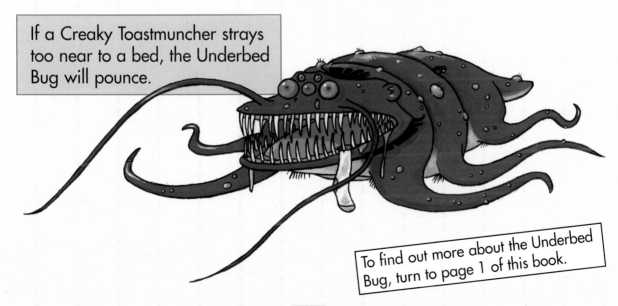

To find out more about the Underbed Bug, turn to page 1 of this book.

Catching Food

The Creaky Toastmuncher creaks as it creeps out of the attic in the middle of the night.

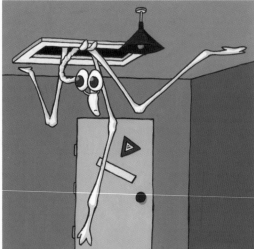

1. When everyone's asleep, the Creaky Toastmuncher sneaks out of hiding.
2. It checks that the coast is clear and then slowly tiptoes down the stairs.
3. It turns the toaster to maximum power, cooks a round of toast, then eats it dry.

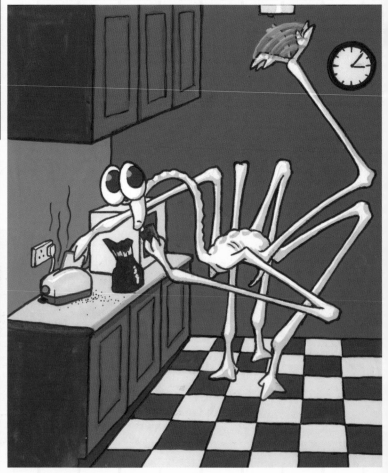

The Creaky Toastmuncher

Life Cycle

Creaky Toastmunchers live alone from an early age. They like it that way.

1. Creaky Toastmunchers are born creaky, but they have to learn how to make toast.	3. The training is complete when the young Toastmuncher reaches its first birthday.
2. When they are four months old Creaky Toastmunchers are trained in the ancient art of toast burning.	4. The newly trained Toastmuncher leaves the attic. It climbs along the phone lines to a new home.

The Creaky Toastmuncher

How to Spot One

This poster about Creaky Toastmunchers explains how to spot them.

Creaky Toastmuncher:
home testing advice

Do you have a problem?

- Do your floorboards creak in the night?

- Is your toaster often on MAX in the morning?

If you answered "yes" to one or more of these questions, you may have a Creaky Toastmuncher living in your home.

Is it a Creaky Toastmuncher?

Attach an "exit alert device" (also called a "bell on a string") to your attic door. If the bell rings in the night, jump out and catch the little tinker.

Collect their weird footprints by leaving a large blob of plasticine on the kitchen floor.

Creaky Toastmuncher footprint

Footprint of a naughty child

The Just-Behind-You Horse

The Just-Behind-You Horse

The Just-Behind-You Horse is a horse, of course... a horse that flies behind you.

Beady Eyes
The Just-Behind-You Horse has great eyesight. It will spot you before you spot it.

Wings
These help people tell it apart from normal horses.

The wings are silent, so the Just-Behind-You Horse can sneak up on people.

The wings are also very strong, so the Just-Behind-You Horse can dart out of sight in a flash.

Long Muzzle
This is for snuffling around in rucksacks.

Legs
These are short and spindly because it hardly ever uses them.

Big Bottom
This is great for balance during flight and for sitting on when resting.

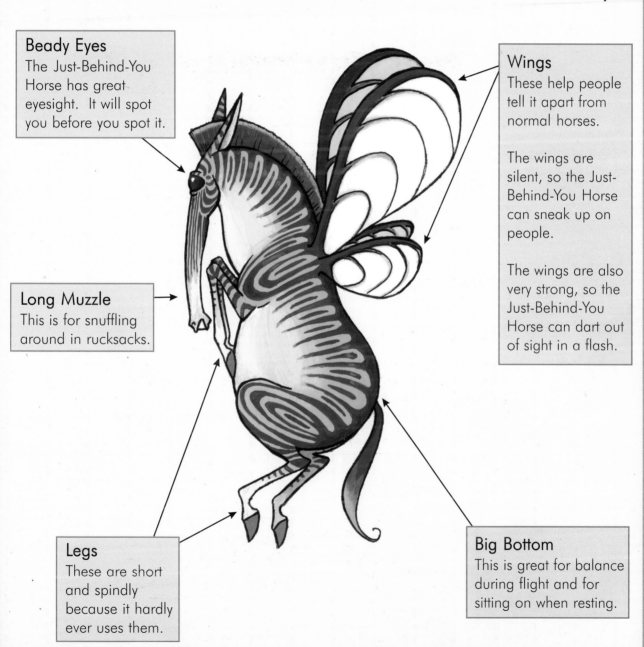

The Just-Behind-You Horse

Food

Just-Behind-You Horses eat lots of things, but they love eggy sandwiches.

AGE	0 to 5	5 to 10	10 to 50
FOOD EATEN	lots and lots of ants	bird fleas and badger ticks	bird eggs and packed lunches

Enemies

Giant Forest Guinea Pigs eat Just-Behind-You Horses, if they can catch them.

9 out of 10 Just-Behind-You Horses are far too quick to be caught by a Giant Forest Guinea Pig.

Find out about the Giant Forest Guinea Pig in the "Monsters from the Country" book.

The Just-Behind-You Horse

Catching Food

Snuffling up eggs is easy, but snuffling up eggy sandwiches is tricky.

Just-Behind-You Horses could just eat bird eggs, but where's the fun in that?

They have much more fun silently stealing sandwiches from rucksacks.

Just-Behind-You Horses hide behind trees. If they spot a walker they fly just behind them.

They undo zips and lunch boxes with their teeth and gobble the sandwiches.

The Just-Behind-You Horse

Life Cycle

As it gets older, the Just-Behind-You Horse annoys bigger and bigger animals.

Up to the age of five, the young Just-Behind-You Horse practices sneaking up on ants.

By the age of seven, it can fly just behind robins.

Before they start stalking humans they practice on angry badgers.

How to Spot One

You have to be cunning and gymnastic to spot a Just-Behind-You Horse.

You won't spot a Just-Behind-You Horse by spinning round quickly. They are far too quick for that.

You need to perfect the "run up a wall somersault" to spot one.

The Just-Behind-You Horse is so impressed by this move that it forgets to follow.

1. Find a wall.
2. Run up the wall.
3. Push off and flip.
4. Land just behind the Just-Behind-You Horse.
   There she is.

The End

This dark, evil-looking critter is called an End. It gives me the creeps.

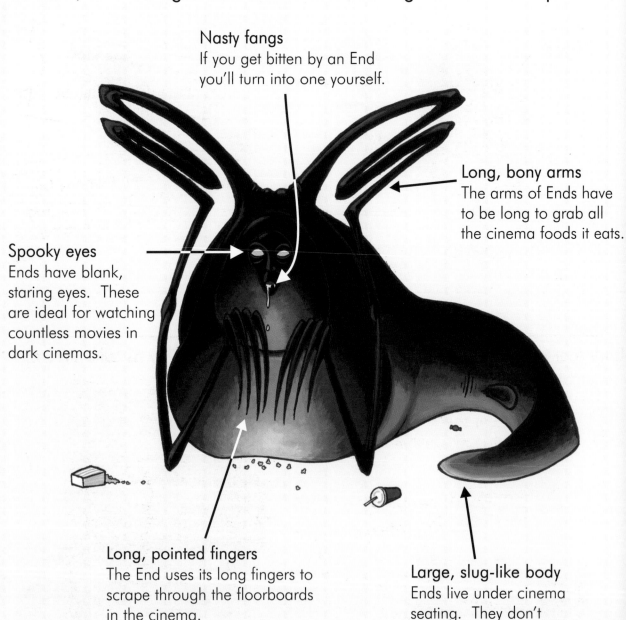

Nasty fangs
If you get bitten by an End you'll turn into one yourself.

Long, bony arms
The arms of Ends have to be long to grab all the cinema foods it eats.

Spooky eyes
Ends have blank, staring eyes. These are ideal for watching countless movies in dark cinemas.

Long, pointed fingers
The End uses its long fingers to scrape through the floorboards in the cinema.

Large, slug-like body
Ends live under cinema seating. They don't have to move very far.

The End

Food

Ends feed on cinema snacks – popcorn, fizzy drinks and chocolate.

sweet popcorn

chocolate hidden in bag

sugary drink

sweets in pocket

JEDI IN TRAINING

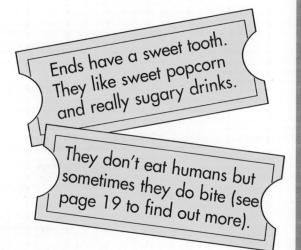

Ends have a sweet tooth. They like sweet popcorn and really sugary drinks.

They don't eat humans but sometimes they do bite (see page 19 to find out more).

Enemies

Ends fear only one man – the pizza delivery hero known only as Luke Warm.

Luke Warm spends weekdays hunting Urban Chameleons.

At the weekends he likes to hunt Ends and wipe them out.

WHOOSH

Find out a bit more about Luke Warm in the "Monsters from the City" book.

The End

Catching Food

The End just reaches out and grabs all the food it needs.

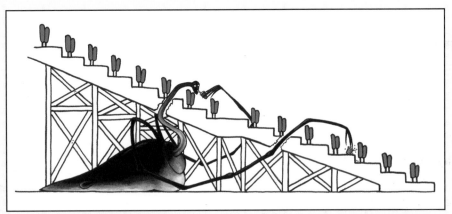

The End's arms grow long enough to reach every corner of the cinema.
The End scratches holes under the seats so it can reach through and watch films.

While everyone is watching the film, the End steals their snacks.

The End is Nigh

The End

Life Cycle

If you stay in the cinema after the film has finished, beware the bite of the End.

1. Ends only bite people who stay in the cinema long after the film has finished.

2. Once bitten, the transformation begins.

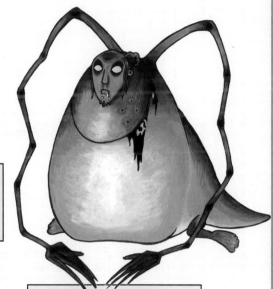

3. The new End looks for a new cinema to live in.

4. The new End settles down in its new home to watch films and eat junk food.

The End

How to Spot One

Ends aren't pretty things to look at, but if you want to spot one, here's how:

Equipment needed:
- Human-sized dummy
- Popcorn, sugary drinks, sweets
- Rope, skateboard, camera
- Dark clothing

Method
1   Make human-shaped dummy.
2   Slump it in a cinema seat and load it up with popcorn, fizzy drinks and sweets.
4   Crouch on the floor behind it and wait for the End.
5   Snap and skate away... quickly.

THE END

Glossary

alien

Any living thing that doesn't come from the Earth. In a lot of films, aliens are tall and grey with big heads and black eyes, but they could look like anything. (They might look like giant goats - see the "Monsters from Space" book.)

attic

The top, spooky bit of some houses. Most of them smell of old dust, have cobwebs everywhere and are full of boxes of Christmas decorations and old junk.

contents

A list of all the pages that are in the book. You can use it to find out which page to turn to.

feelers

Long thin things, like tentacles. They are used for feeling things, not for grabbing them.

glossary

That's this page in the book. It lists all the complicated words in the book and explains what they mean.

index

That's the next page. It lists everything in the book and tells you which page it's on.

innards

A name for all the bits inside your body — your heart, lungs, stomach, intestines, the lot.

introduction

The introduction tells you what the book is about. It goes right at the start of the book.

tentacles

Long, thin, bendy, armlike things used for grabbing. Octopuses and squid have eight tentacles each.

Index